Exploring The
# BUILDING BLOCKS
of
# Science

## Book 4
## TEACHER'S MANUAL

# REBECCA W. KELLER, PhD

Exploring the Building Blocks of Science Book 4 Teacher's Manual
ISBN 978-1-941181-07-2

Published by Gravitas Publications Inc.
www.realscience4kids.com
www.gravitaspublications.com

# A Note From the Author

This curriculum is designed for elementary level students and provides an introduction to the scientific disciplines of chemistry, biology, physics, geology, and astronomy. *Exploring the Building Blocks of Science Book 4 Laboratory Notebook* accompanies *Exploring the Building Blocks of Science Book 4 Student Textbook.* Together, both provide students with basic science concepts needed for developing a solid framework for real science investigation. The *Laboratory Notebook* contains 44 experiments—two experiments for each chapter of the Student Textbook. These experiments allow students to further explore concepts presented in the *Student Textbook.* This teacher's manual will help you guide students through laboratory experiments designed to help them develop the skills needed for the first step in the scientific method — making good observations.

There are several sections in each chapter of the *Laboratory Notebook.* The section called *Think About It* provides questions to help students develop critical thinking skills and spark their imagination. The *Observe It* section helps students explore how to make good observations. In every chapter there is a *What Did You Discover?* section that gives the students an opportunity to summarize the observations they have made. A section called *Why?* provides a short explanation of what students may or may not have observed. And finally, in each chapter an additional experiment is presented in *Just For Fun.*

The experiments take up to 1 hour. The materials needed for each experiment are listed on the following pages and also at the beginning of each experiment.

Enjoy!

*Rebecca W. Keller, PhD*

# Materials at a Glance

| Experiment 1 | Experiment 2 | Experiment 3 | Experiment 5 | Experiment 6 |
|---|---|---|---|---|
| An old used cell phone that is no longer needed. If a used cell phone cannot be located, you can substitute any other electronic device, such as an old computer or electronic toy.<br><br>a second electronic device to take apart<br><br>rubber gloves, 1-2 pairs | colored pencils, crayons, or markers<br>jelly beans of different colors:<br>  red<br>  gray (lavender can be used)<br>  blue<br>  black<br>  green<br>  white<br>  [or substitute objects such as those listed below]<br>*Just For Fun* section: objects of different colors—at least 10 of each color, it can be food (like M&M's, jelly beans, etc., or objects like buttons, beads, or marbles); red and gray are the important colors | water<br>1-2 ice cube trays or paper cups<br>small frying pan or saucepan with lid<br>pot holder<br>2 Styrofoam cups<br>freezer<br>stove | 2 raw eggs<br>2 bowls<br>fork<br>2 plastic bags<br>frying pan<br>1 ice cube<br>stove<br>freezer | notebook for student to make into a biologist's field notebook<br>pencil, pen<br>colored pencils<br>**Optional**<br>camera<br>backpack<br>snack and bottle of water |

### Experiment 4

8 Styrofoam cups
360 ml (1 1/2 cups) boiling water
240 ml (1 cup) cold tap water
60 ml (4 Tbsp) baking soda
120 ml (1/2 cup) apple cider vinegar
120 ml (1/2 cup) balsamic vinegar
measuring cup and spoons
spoon
stove

| Experiment 7 | Experiment 8 | Experiment 9 | Experiment 10 | Experiment 11 |
|---|---|---|---|---|
| large tray or plastic box, at least .3 m (1 ft.) on each side, and cover<br>garden dirt (with lots of organic material)<br>spoon or garden trowel<br>holding box for the snails/worms to keep them moist and dark<br>12 snails/slugs and/or 20–40 worms *<br>water<br>experimental snail and worm barriers. Set the amount you are going to use in an open container in the sun for a few days.<br>table or rock salt plus three of the following:<br>cinnamon<br>baking soda<br>black pepper<br>cornstarch<br>flour<br>borax<br>an active anthill | butterfly kit<br>small cage<br><br>Butterfly kits can be purchased from a variety of different sources, such as:<br><br>Home Science Tools:<br>www.hometrainingtools.com<br><br>Insect Lore:<br>www.insectlore.com | tadpole kit (or tadpoles or frog eggs collected locally)<br><br>A tadpole kit can be purchased from Home Science Tools:<br>www.hometrainingtools.com.<br><br>aquarium<br>water<br>tadpole food | chalk in different colors<br>narrow rope or heavy string about .6 m (2 ft.) long - heavy enough to move along the ground when one end is wiggled | 5 identical glass jars or drinking glasses<br>water<br>wooden drumstick, ruler, wooden spoon, or other wooden stick<br>flat, unobstructed area for playing a game<br>**Optional**<br>blindfold |

* Look for online or local sources of snails and/or earthworms. Or you and your students may be able to collect them yourselves.

| Experiment 12 | Experiment 13 | Experiment 14 | Experiment 15 | Experiment 16 |
|---|---|---|---|---|
| two prisms (glass or plastic)<br>flashlight<br>sunlight<br>white wall, whiteboard, or other white surface<br>colored pencils | 3 small jars<br>180 ml (3/4 cup) vegetable oil<br>120 ml (1/2 cup) water<br>120 ml (1/2 cup) acetone (nail polish remover)<br>food coloring<br>drinking glass (a square glass is preferred, but a round glass will work)<br>thin wooden stick (e.g., a kebab skewer)<br>marking pen (or paper and tape) to label jars | large balloon (may substitute plastic wrap)<br>glass jar<br>scissors<br>rubber band<br>plastic straw<br>toothpick<br>tape<br>index card<br>**Optional**<br>piece of cardboard | scissors<br>tape<br>2 small baskets, hats, or other containers to hold game pieces<br>pair of dice<br>**Optional**<br>colored pencils | Two renewable resources model kits chosen from list provided. (See first page of Exper. 16) |

| Experiment 17 | Experiment 18 | Experiment 19 | Experiment 21 | Experiment 22 |
|---|---|---|---|---|
| **Optional**<br>small notebook | model rocket kit (1 or more)—see list of suggested kits at beginning of experiment<br>tools for assembly depending on kit selected<br><br>Note: Other kits may be substituted | tape<br>scissors<br>marking pen<br>**Optional**<br>2-3 push pins or tacks | Robot kit —see list of suggested kits at beginning of experiment | *Laboratory Notebook* |

| Experiment 20 |
|---|
| computer with internet access |

# Materials
## Quantities Needed for All Experiments

| Equipment | Equipment (Continued) | Foods |
|---|---|---|
| aquarium<br>bowls, 2<br>box to hold snails/worms to keep them moist and dark<br>cage, small, for butterfly<br>cell phone (old used) that is no longer needed. If a used cell phone cannot be located, you can substitute any other electronic device, such as an old computer or electronic toy.<br>computer with internet access<br>containers, 2 small (baskets, hats, or other containers to hold game pieces)<br>dice, 1 pair<br>electronic device to take apart<br>flashlight<br>fork<br>freezer<br>frying pan (small) or saucepan with lid<br>garden trowel or spoon<br>glass, drinking (a square glass is preferred, but a round glass will work)<br>ice cube trays (1-2) or paper cups<br>jars, 3 small<br>jars (glass) or drinking glasses, 5 identical<br>measuring cup<br>measuring spoons<br>oven mitt or pot holder<br>prisms (glass or plastic), 2<br>scissors<br>spoon<br>stick, wooden (drumstick, ruler, wooden spoon, or other wooden stick)<br>stick, wooden, thin (e.g., a kebab skewer)<br>stove<br>tray, large , or plastic box, at least .3 m (1 ft.) on each side, and cover | **Kits**<br><br>kits, 2, renewable resources model kits chosen from list provided (See Experiment 16)<br>kit, model rocket  (1 or more)—see list of suggested kits - Experiment 18<br>kit, robot —see list of suggested kits  - Experiment 21<br><br>**Misc.**<br><br>tools for kit assembly, depending on kit<br><br><br>**Optional**<br><br>backpack<br>blindfold<br>camera | baking soda, 60 ml (4 Tbsp)<br>eggs, raw, 2<br>ice cube, 1<br>jelly beans of different colors:<br>    red<br>    gray (lavender can be used)<br>    blue<br>    black<br>    green<br>    white<br>    [or substitute other colored objects—see Experiment 2]<br>snack and bottle of water<br>vegetable oil, 180 ml (3/4 cup)<br>vinegar, apple cider, 120 ml (1/2 cup)<br>vinegar, balsamic, 120 ml (1/2 cup) |

# Materials
## Quantities Needed for All Experiments

| Materials | Materials (continued) | Other |
|---|---|---|
| acetone (nail polish remover), 120 ml (1/2 cup)<br>bags, plastic, 2<br>balloon, large (may substitute plastic wrap)<br>card, index, 1-2<br>chalk, different colors<br>cups, Styrofoam, 10<br>dirt, garden (with lots of organic material)<br>food coloring<br>notebook for student to make into a biologist's field notebook<br>pen<br>pen, marking<br>pencil<br>pencils (colored)<br>rope (narrow) or heavy string, about .6 m (2 ft.) long—heavy enough to move along the ground when one end is wiggled<br>rubber band, 1<br>rubber gloves, 1-2 pairs<br>straw, plastic, 1<br>tape<br>toothpick, 1<br>water<br>water, boiling, 360 ml (1 1/2 cups)<br>water, cold tap, 240 ml (1 cup) | **Misc.**<br>experimental snail and worm barriers. (Set the amount you are going to use in an open container in the sun for a few days.)<br>table or rock salt plus 3 of the following:<br>cinnamon<br>baking soda<br>black pepper<br>cornstarch<br>flour<br>borax<br>objects of different colors—at least 10 of each color, it can be food (like M&M's, jelly beans, etc.) or objects like buttons, beads, or marbles; red and gray are the important colors<br><br>**Optional**<br>cardboard, 1 piece<br>crayons or markers<br>notebook, small<br>push pins or tacks, 2-3 | anthill, active<br>area (flat, unobstructed) for playing a game<br>snails/slugs (12) and/or 20–40 worms *<br>sunlight<br>tadpole food<br>wall (white), whiteboard, or other white surface<br><br>**Kits**<br>butterfly kit (can be purchased from a variety of different sources, such as:<br>Home Science Tools: www.hometrainingtools.com)<br>Insect Lore: www.insectlore.com<br>tadpole kit (or tadpoles or frog eggs collected locally)<br>A tadpole kit can be purchased from Home Science Tools: www.hometrainingtools.com |

* Look for online or local sources of snails and/or earthworms. Or you and your students may be able to collect them yourselves.

# Contents

# Get Inside a Cell Phone!

## Materials Needed

- An old, used cell phone, preferably one that is no longer needed. If a used cell phone cannot be located, you can substitute any other electronic device, such as an old computer or electronic toy.
- a second electronic device to take apart
- rubber gloves, 1–2 pairs

## Objectives

In this experiment, students will disassemble a modern technological item and explore how scientific discoveries are needed for technology.

The objectives of this lesson are for students to:

- Observe how science contributes to technology.
- Explore a modern technological device.

## Experiment

### I. Think About It

Read this section of the *Laboratory Notebook* with your students.

Explore open inquiry with questions such as the following:

- *How do you think a cell phone works?*

- *What do you think a cell phone is made of?*

- *Do you think the cell phone has changed over time? Why or why not?*

- *How do you think cell phones will change? (get smaller? thinner? lighter? perform more functions?)*

### II. Observe It

Read this section of the *Laboratory Notebook* with your students.

In this experiment students will disassemble a cell phone and examine its components. The item does not need to be taken apart completely. Many cell phones will have a back, a battery, and a SIM card that can be removed. It is OK to stop here, but if the cell phone or device can be destroyed, allow the student to pry open the back or front with supervision.

Supervise the students and have them wear rubber gloves while doing this experiment.

❶-❷ Have the students take the back off a used cell phone and examine the components.

❸ Have the students draw the inside of the cell phone.

❹-❺ Help the students identify the SIM card (memory chip) and the battery and then carefully remove them. Don't let them try to take the battery apart.

❻ Have your students further disassemble the cell phone, if possible, without destroying any of the components.

❼ Have the students draw all the components they removed from the cell phone and label each with the materials they think it is made of and whether or not they think it is part of an electronic circuit.

## III. What Did You Discover?

Read this section of the *Laboratory Notebook* with your students.

Have the students answer the questions. There are no right answers and their answers will depend on what they actually observed.

## IV. Why?

Read this section of the *Laboratory Notebook* with your students.
Discuss any questions that might come up.

## V. Just For Fun

Supervise the students while they take apart another electronic device. Have them carefully remove as many components as possible. They should again wear rubber gloves.

There is a box provided for them to draw the components they've removed and to write their observations about how the components of the cell phone and the second device are similar and how they are different.

# Experiment 2

## To Share or Not To Share

**Materials Needed**

- colored pencils, crayons, or markers
- jelly beans of different colors:
  red
  gray (lavender can be used)
  blue
  black
  green
  white
  [or substitute objects such as those listed below]
- *Just For Fun* section:
  objects of different colors—at least 10 of each color. These can be food (like M&Ms, jelly beans, etc.) or objects like buttons, beads, or marbles. Red and gray are the important colors.

## Objectives

In this experiment, students will explore chemical reactions and model building.

The objectives of this lesson are for students to understand that:

- Scientists use different kinds of investigations (like model building) depending on the questions they are trying to answer.
- Scientists develop explanations by using observations.

## Experiment

### I. Think About It

Read this section of the *Laboratory Notebook* with your students.

Explore open inquiry with the following:

- *What types of models have you used? (models of cars, planes, boats, horses, etc.)*

- *How have these models helped you understand how things work?*

- *What limitations do these models have?*

- *What different materials could you use to build models?*

- *What models would you like to build that would help you learn more? What do you think you might learn?*

### II. Observe It

Read this section of the *Laboratory Notebook* with your students.

Have your students build the atoms and molecules in the experiment. Have them make colored drawings of their results.

In the following illustrations, each circle is the center of an atom, and the black dots represent the bonding electrons (red jelly beans). The jelly beans don't need to be positioned exactly like those in the illustrations, but the bonds should be paired as shown.

Step ❶   lithium atom

CHEMISTRY

Step ❷   fluorine atom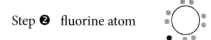

Step ❸   lithium fluoride molecule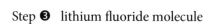

Step ❹   4 hydrogen atoms

Step ❺   carbon atom

Step ❻   methane molecule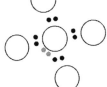

Step ❼   oxygen

2 hydrogens

water molecule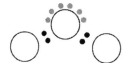

## III. What Did You Discover?

Read this section of the *Laboratory Notebook* with your students.

Have the students answer the questions. Answers are as follows:

❶  2

❷  8

❸  4 bonds are formed. The bonds are covalent because hydrogen and carbon share electrons.

❹  4

❺  2

## IV. Why?

Read this section of the *Laboratory Notebook* with your students.
Discuss any questions that might come up.

## V. Just For Fun

Have students review this chapter in the *Student Textbook* and find some atoms and molecules they would like to model. Provide objects of different colors, including red and gray. Have students make colored drawings of their molecule models and label the atoms and molecules with their names.

# Experiment 3

# Three States of Water

**Materials Needed**

- water
- 1-2 ice cube trays or paper cups
- small frying pan or saucepan with lid
- pot holder
- 2 Styrofoam cups
- freezer
- stove

## Objectives

In this experiment students will observe how water changes from one state to another and how its properties change.

The objectives of this lesson are for students to observe that:

- Materials exist in different states: solid, liquid, and gas.
- Some common materials, such as water, can be changed from one state to another by heating or cooling.

## Experiment

### I. Think About It

Read this section of the *Laboratory Notebook* with your students.

Have the students think about water and what they have observed about it. Guide open inquiry with questions such as the following:

- *Where do you think you would find liquid water?*

- *Where do you think you would find water in its solid state?*

- *Where do you think you would find water in its gaseous state?*

- *Do you think all the different states of water occur in nature? Do you think this is important? Why or why not?*

- *How do you think you could get water to change from a liquid to a solid? To a gas?*

### II. Observe It

Read this section of the *Laboratory Notebook* with your students.

❶ Have students fill an ice cube tray or partially fill a paper cup and then test the liquid water with their senses. What does it look like, feel like, what shape is it, etc.  Have them record their observations.

❷ Help students put the ice cube tray or paper cup in the freezer and leave it until the water is frozen. Then have them test the ice with their senses and record their observations.

❸ Help students put the ice in a small frying pan or saucepan on a stove with the heat on low or medium. Have them observe what happens to the ice as it melts and then record their observations.

❹ Help the students bring the water to a boil and then put the lid on the pan. Leave it for a few minutes and then have the students use a pot holder to take the lid off or do it for them. Have them observe the inside of the lid, which should have condensed water on it.

## III. What Did You Discover?

Read this section of the *Laboratory Notebook* with your students.

Have the students refer to their experimental observations as they answer the questions. There are no right answers, and their answers will depend on what they actually observed.

## IV. Why?

Read this section of the *Laboratory Notebook* with your students.
Discuss any questions that might come up.

## V. Just For Fun

In this experiment students will perform a test to see if hot water freezes faster than cold water. The experiment calls for the students to direct the teacher to perform the steps that call for handling boiling water.

The expected result is for students to find out that hot water freezes faster than cold water. Although scientists have theories, so far it is uncertain why this happens. Maybe your student will be the one to find out!

# Experiment 4

## Fast or Slow?

**Materials Needed**

- 8 Styrofoam cups
- 360 ml (1 1/2 cups) boiling water
- 240 ml (1 cup) cold tap water
- 60 ml (4 Tbsp.) baking soda
- 120 ml (1/2 cup) apple cider vinegar
- 120 ml (1/2 cup) balsamic vinegar
- measuring cup and spoons
- spoon
- stove

## Objectives

In this experiment students will observe how using more or less heat can change the speed of a chemical reaction.

The objectives of this lesson are for students to:

- Observe that substances react chemically in characteristic ways with other substances to form new substances.
- Understand that chemical elements do not break down during normal laboratory reactions.

## Experiment

### I. Think About It

Read this section of the *Laboratory Notebook* with your students.

Have the students think about what they have learned about how chemical reactions are affected by heat. Guide open inquiry with questions such as the following:

- *Do you think adding heat can make a chemical reaction happen faster? Why or why not?*

- *Do you think taking away heat (making things colder) might make a chemical reaction happen faster? Why or why not?*

- *Do you think chemical reactions can happen to foods that you cook? Why or why not? Have you observed any?*

- *Do you think chemical reactions always happen when you cook food? Why or why not?*

- *Do you think chemical reactions can happen to things that are in the freezer? Why or why not?*

### II. Observe It

Read this section of the *Laboratory Notebook* with your students.

Before starting this experiment, bring at least 360 ml (1 1/2 cups) of water to a boil. You will need to use 240 ml (1 cup) for both experiments.

❶ Have students measure 60 ml (1/4 cup) of apple cider vinegar into each of 2 Styrofoam cups.

❷ Have students run tap water until it is cold and then measure 120 ml (1/2 cup) of cold tap water into a Styrofoam cup.

❸ Have students measure 15 ml (1 Tbsp.) baking soda, add it to the cup of cold water, and stir to dissolve.

❹ Measure 120 ml (1/2 cup) of boiling water and pour it into a Styrofoam cup for the students.

❺ Have students measure 15 ml (1 Tbsp.) baking soda, carefully add it to the cup of boiling water, and stir to dissolve. Have students observe whether the baking soda dissolves more easily in hot or cold water. This amount of baking soda may not dissolve completely in either cup.

❻ Have students pick up the 2 cups that contain vinegar, and at the same time, pour the contents of each cup into one of the cups of baking soda water.

❼ Have them record their observations in the space provided.

## III. What Did You Discover?

Read this section of the *Laboratory Notebook* with your students.

Have students answer the questions based on what they actually observed rather than what they thought might happen. There are no right answers.

## IV. Why?

Read this section of the *Laboratory Notebook* with your students.
Discuss any questions that might come up.

## V. Just For Fun

Have students repeat the experiment with balsamic vinegar instead of apple cider vinegar.

In general, balsamic vinegar creates a more pronounced reaction because most balsamic vinegar contains sugar, which doesn't react but makes the bubbles in the reaction last longer.

# Experiment 5

## Eggs—Hot or Cold?

**Materials Needed**

- 2 raw eggs
- 2 bowls
- fork
- 2 plastic bags
- frying pan
- 1 ice cube
- stove
- freezer

## Objectives

In this experiment students will observe how adding heat to a raw scrambled egg causes a chemical reaction and taking away heat from a raw scrambled egg causes a change of state.

The objectives of this lesson are for students to observe that:

- A substance has characteristic properties, such as density, a boiling point, and stability.
- Substances react chemically in characteristic ways with other substances to form new compounds.

## Experiment

## I. Think About It

Read this section of the *Laboratory Notebook* with your students.

Have students think about what they've learned about chemical reactions and heat. Guide open inquiry with questions such as the following:

- *Would you rather eat a cooked egg or a raw egg? Why?*

- *Do you think an egg is the same before and after it is cooked? Why or why not?*

- *Do you think you would get the same results by cooking a raw egg and freezing a raw egg? Why or why not?*

- *What do you think would happen to a raw egg if you froze it and then thawed it out? Why?*

- *What do you think would happen if you froze a raw egg, then thawed it and cooked it? Why?*

- *What do you think would happen if you froze a cooked egg and thawed it out? Why?*

## II. Observe It

Read this section of the *Laboratory Notebook* with your students.

❶ Have students take 2 raw eggs, break each into a separate bowl, and beat with a fork.

❷ Have students put one of the scrambled eggs in a plastic bag, seal the bag, and put it in the freezer.

CHEMISTRY

❸    Help students cook the other raw egg. Set it aside.

❹    When the egg in the freezer is frozen, have the students remove it from the freezer and let it thaw without heating it.

❺-❻ Have students observe the properties of the cooked egg and the thawed egg  and record their observations.

❼ Help the students cook the egg that was frozen and observe and compare both cooked eggs.

❽    Have them record their observations.

## III. What Did You Discover?

Read this section of the *Laboratory Notebook* with your students.

Have students answer the questions based on what they actually observed rather than what they thought might happen. There are no right answers.

## IV. Why?

Read this section of the *Laboratory Notebook* with your students.
Discuss any questions that might come up.

## V. Just For Fun

Have the students take an ice cube, place it in a plastic bag, and seal the bag. Have the students hold the plastic bag in their hands and watch as the ice melts. They can move the ice cube from one hand to the other if their hands get too cold. They will observe heat transferring from their hands to the ice cube. The "evidence" of heat transference is the observation that the ice cube is melting and their hands are cooling.

# Experiment 6
## Nature Walk

**Materials Needed**

- notebook for student to make into a biologist's field notebook
- pencil, pen
- colored pencils

**Optional**

- camera
- backpack
- snack and bottle of water

## Objectives

In this experiment students will observe animals in their environment.

The objectives of this lesson are for students to:

- Explore the basic needs of animals—air, water, and food.
- Examine different animals in the environment.

## Experiment

### I. Think About It

Read this section of the *Laboratory Notebook* with your students.

Have the students think about animals they have already observed. Explore open inquiry with questions such as the following:

- *What kinds of animals have you seen in your house, yard, and environment?*

- *What things have you seen animals eat?*

- *What kinds of animals have you eaten, if any?*

- *What features have you observed in animals? (hair, eyes, legs, etc.)*

- *In what different ways do animals move?*

- *Do you think animals can communicate with each other? Why or why not? If so, how?*

- *In what ways are animals different from plants?*

### II. Observe It

Read this section of the *Laboratory Notebook* with your students.

In this experiment students will explore making a biologist's field notebook for their observations about animals. A biologist's field notebook can contain items such as written notes, drawings, and photographs. Students will use their field notebook in several experiments.

Take your students on a nature walk or to a zoo and help them observe the animals around them. Have them notice size, shape, color, and other features, such as type of hair, feathers or scales, and shape of ears and tail, etc. Help them pick one or two animals to study closely. Encourage students to draw  at least one of the animals they see. They will notice more features if they attempt to draw the animal than if they only take a photograph.

BIOLOGY

## III. What Did You Discover?

Read this section of the *Laboratory Notebook* with your students.

Have the students refer to their field notebook as they answer the questions. There are no right answers and their answers will depend on what they actually observed.

## IV. Why?

Read this section of the *Laboratory Notebook* with your students.
Discuss any questions that might come up.

## V. Just For Fun

Students will continue to add their observations to their field notebook, observing animals over the course of several months to see how animals grow and change and how their activities differ with the seasons. Students can add more animals to observe.

Encourage students to look for features and behaviors they may not have noticed before. They may also see animals they did not notice previously. Drawing the animals is a good tool for making detailed observations.

BIOLOGY

# Experiment 7

# Red Light, Green Light

**Materials Needed**

- large tray or plastic box, at least .3 meter (1 ft) on each side
- something big enough to cover the tray
- garden dirt (lots of organic material is important for worms)
- spoon or garden trowel
- holding box for the snails/worms that keeps them moist and dark
- 12 snails/slugs and/or 20–40 worms
- water
- Experimental snail and worm barriers. If you can, set the amount of powder you are going to use in an open container in the sun for a few days.
- Use table or rock salt and choose three from the following list:
  cinnamon
  baking soda
  black pepper
  cornstarch
  flour
  borax
- an active anthill

## Objectives

In this experiment, students will observe external cues that influence animal behavior.

The objectives of this lesson are for students to:

- Examine how animals detect external cues.
- Explore how an organism's environment influences its behavior.

## Experiment

## I. Think About It

Read this section of the *Laboratory Notebook* with your students.

Have the student think about animals they have already observed.

Explore open inquiry with questions such as the following:

- *What is an earthworm?*
- *What is a snail?*
- *How are they similar?*
- *How are they different?*
- *How do you think earthworms and snails would respond to a barrier that's put in their way?*
- *Do you think earthworms and snails will both respond to a barrier in a similar way? Why or why not?*

## II. Observe It

Read this section of the *Laboratory Notebook* with your students.

You can use both snails and earthworms for this experiment, or you can choose one or the other. The experiment can also be done with slugs.

Snails are readily found in the late spring and summer months in many parts of the world. Earthworms can be ordered year-round in most parts of the United States, however, the availability in other countries will vary. Some investigators claim that European earthworms are hardier than red wigglers, but red wigglers are cheaper. If you plan to keep your worms inside and alive for more than a few days, look for advice. Worm-selling companies and other enthusiasts will share their knowledge on how to build and prepare a suitable habitat and how to feed and care for the worms. Worms can be kept for months on moist newspaper and fed kitchen scraps. They do not smell and will make compost for plants.

Be sure to protect the experiment from cold or heat. Cold will stop the subjects from moving, and heat will kill them. You could use direct sunlight to encourage snails to go in the right direction. While worms have no eyes but only light sensors scattered across their body, snails have primitive eyes. Snails are capable of climbing vertical surfaces and can even climb over a knife blade without injuring themselves.

❶ Help students put enough dirt in the plastic box or tray to completely cover the bottom.

❷ Have the students add some water to the dirt in one-half of the box, being careful to add only enough to make the dirt moist and not soggy. The dirt in the other half of the box needs to stay as dry as possible.

❸ Have students perform a control experiment by placing the subjects on the dry side of the box. Here, the snails/earthworms will be responding to conditions that are likely to happen in nature. It's expected that they will move from the dry area to the moist area. Have students record their observations.

❹-❿ Help students carefully move the subjects from the box with dirt to the holding box between each part of the experiment.

Students are to pour a line of one of the powders on top of the dirt and from one side of the box to the other, dividing the dry and moist areas. Before they use a different powder, have them carefully remove the old powder and put more dirt in the area they have dug out.

Have students use salt as one of the powders. The expected results are that a few worms may go into the salt barrier, while snails should not be willing to cross a barrier of salt. Salt draws moisture out of tissues, which is deadly to both of these creatures. When encountering salt, the snails start to foam. This is a defensive reaction that is not directly caused by the salt.

Snails are generally unwilling to cross any of the substances on the list except for flour and cornstarch.

When encountering substances such as cinnamon and pepper, snails merely pull in their tentacles and head off in another direction or hide inside their shells.

## III. What Did You Discover?

Read this section of the *Laboratory Notebook* with your students.

Have the students refer to their experimental observations as they answer the questions. There are no right answers and their answers will depend on what they actually observed.

## IV. Why?

Read this section of the *Laboratory Notebook* with your students.

Discuss any questions that might come up.

## V. Just For Fun

In this section students will design their own experiment to see if there are barriers that ants will not cross. Have students review the steps in the snail/earthworm experiment and then write the steps for their own experiment based on those. Help them find an active anthill to use in this experiment. They can use the same substances as for the snail/earthworm experiment or they may want to choose different foods or nontoxic household substances.

Allow students to explore their ideas. There is no right answer to this experiment.

# Butterflies Flutter By

**Materials Needed**

- butterfly kit
- small cage

Butterfly kits can be purchased from a variety of different sources, such as:

Home Science Tools:
www.hometrainingtools.com

Insect Lore:
www.insectlore.com

## Objectives

In this experiment students will observe a caterpillar turning into a butterfly.

The objectives of this lesson are for students to:

- Make careful observations of the metamorphosis of a butterfly.
- Learn about a life cycle.

## Experiment

## I. Think About It

Read this section of the *Laboratory Notebook* with your students.

❶ Have students think about how a butterfly got its name. Help them look up the origin of the butterfly name from a library or internet reference.

Have them make a drawing of how they think the butterfly got its name.

❷ Have the students think about how a caterpillar turns into a butterfly. Guide their exploration of their ideas with questions such as:

- *What do you think happens first when a caterpillar changes to a butterfly?*

- *What do you think happens next when a caterpillar changes to a butterfly?*

- *What do you think happens last when a caterpillar changes to a butterfly?*

- *Do you think you can watch the caterpillar in the chrysalis as it changes to a butterfly?*

- *What do you think the chrysalis is made of?*

- *What color do you think the chrysalis will be?*

Have the students make a drawing of how they think a caterpillar turns into a butterfly.

BIOLOGY

## II. Observe It

Read this section of the *Laboratory Notebook* with your students.

Have the students:

- Follow the instructions to set up the butterfly kit.
- Make careful observations of the different stages of metamorphosis. If they are starting with a chrysalis rather than eggs, help them find pictures of butterfly eggs online or in the library.
- Draw the life cycle of the butterfly as they observe it.
- Write or draw any other interesting observations.

## III. What Did You Discover?

Read this section of the *Laboratory Notebook* with your students.

Have students write summary statements of what they actually observed. They may have expected something different to happen, but encourage them to record what actually happened—even if the butterflies did not grow or the eggs or chrysalis died.

## IV. Why?

Read this section of the *Laboratory Notebook* with your students.

Help the students understand that the life cycle of a butterfly is a very amazing process. Explain to them that if scientists did not make careful observations, they would not know that a caterpillar and a butterfly are the same creature and would not know about the life cycle of a butterfly.

Discuss the origin of the name *butterfly*.

Have the students discuss some reasons why they think scientists might not always be in agreement and why careful observations are important.

## V. Just For Fun

Observing living things in their habitat is an important part of the study of biology. Help your students review this chapter in the *Student Textbook* and write down some features of arthropods in their field notebook. Have them bring their field notebook with them on a nature walk in a park, wooded area, or around the yard. Help them find arthropods in nature and guide them in identifying different stages in arthropod life cycles. Have them add notes and drawings about what they observe.

# Experiment 9

## Tadpoles To Frogs

### Materials Needed

- tadpole kit (or tadpoles or frog eggs collected locally)
  A tadpole kit can be purchased from Home Science Tools at:
  www.hometrainingtools.com.
- aquarium
- water
- tadpole food

### Objectives

In this unit students will observe a tadpole turning into an adult frog.

The objectives of this lesson are for students to:

- Make careful observations of the metamorphosis of a frog.
- Learn about a life cycle.

### Experiment

## I. Think About It

Read this section of the *Laboratory Notebook* with your students.

❶ Have the students think about how the frog got its name. Help them look up the origin of the name *frog* in a library or internet reference source.

Have the students make a drawing of how they think the frog got its name.

❷ Have the students think about how a tadpole turns into a frog. Help them explore their ideas with questions such as:

- *What do you think happens first when a tadpole changes to a frog?*
- *What do you think happens next when a tadpole changes to a frog?*
- *What do you think happens last when a tadpole changes to a frog?*
- *Do you think you can watch the tadpole as it changes to a frog?*
- *What do you think the tadpole will eat when it becomes a frog?*
- *What color do you think the adult frog will be?*

Have the students draw their idea of what will happen as a tadpole changes into a frog.

## II. Observe It

Read this section of the *Laboratory Notebook* with your students.

Guide the students in setting up the tadpole kit. If you have collected tadpoles or frog eggs locally, you can find instructions for their care and feeding on the internet or at the library.

Help the students follow the directions included in the kit or obtained online.

BIOLOGY

For Step ❶: If students are beginning with tadpoles rather than frog eggs, have them find pictures of frog eggs online or at the library.

Have the students observe the growth of a tadpole into a frog. Help them make careful observations and drawings, noting how the tadpole changes.

## III. What Did You Discover?

Read this section of the *Laboratory Notebook* with your students.

Have the students answer the questions about the life cycle of a frog. Help them write summary statements about what they actually observed. They may have expected something different to happen, but encourage them to record what actually did happen — even if the frogs did not grow, or the eggs or tadpoles died.

## IV. Why?

Read this section of the *Laboratory Notebook* with your students.

Discuss any questions that might come up.

Help the students understand that the life cycle of a frog is a very amazing process. Have a discussion about the meaning of metamorphosis as it applies to the frog life cycle.

Explain to the students that scientists would not know about the life cycle of a frog if they did not make careful observations. In the same way, careful observations by the students showed them that a tadpole and a frog are the same creature. They also could see the changes that take place during metamorphosis.

## V. Just For Fun

In this experiment students are asked to go outside and look for frogs, toads, lizards, snakes, birds, and fish in different stages of their life cycle. A trip could be taken to a nearby park, wooded area, aquarium, fish hatchery, zoo, or botanical garden.

Students are to make notes and drawings of their observations in their field notebook.

BIOLOGY

# Experiment 10

# Making Waves

**Materials Needed**

- chalk in different colors
- narrow rope or heavy string about .6 m (2 ft.) long – heavy enough to move along the ground when one end is wiggled

## Objectives

In this experiment, students will observe how to create a transverse wave and how the amplitude and wavelength can be changed.

The objectives of this lesson are for students to observe that:

- Energy can be transferred from one place to another in a wave.
- As energy moves through a wave, matter is not transferred.

## Experiment

## I. Think About It

Read this section of the *Laboratory Notebook* with your students.

Have the students think about waves they have already observed in water and other waves they have seen.

Explore open inquiry with questions such as the following:

- *What happens to water when a pebble is dropped into it? Why?*

- *If you jumped in the water, would you make a bigger or smaller wave than a pebble? a boulder? Why?*

- *What other waves have you observed? What did they look like?*

- *Can you make a wave in oil? Why or why not?*

- *Can you make a wave in molasses? Why or why not?*

- *Have you ever been in a stadium wave? What did you notice?*

- *Have you ever been in a boat on the waves? What did you notice?*

## II. Observe It

Read this section of the *Laboratory Notebook* with your students.

The rope or string used in this experiment should be heavy enough that it will move when one end is wiggled.

❶-❷ Use one color of chalk. Help the students crush the colored chalk and spread the chalk powder on a flat surface. A flat sidewalk outside will work well. If that is not possible, an area on a table or counter top can be used.

PHYSICS

❸ Have the students carefully place the rope or string across the middle of the chalk powder so the chalk powder is not disturbed.

❹-❺ Have the students lift one end of the rope to see the mark it leaves in the chalk dust. Then have them write about or draw their observations in the box provided.

❻-❼ Have the students smooth out the chalk dust and again place the rope across the middle of the dust. Then have them take one end of the rope and wiggle it gently to create a wave. Have them lift the rope off the chalk dust and record their observations. They should observe the chalk dust moving away from the string, creating a pattern. The peaks of the wave should be visible.

❽-❾ Have the students repeat Steps ❻-❼, this time wiggling the rope vigorously. Have them record their observations.

In this experiment students created a transverse wave with the rope.

## III. What Did You Discover?

Read this section of the *Laboratory Notebook* with your students.

Have the students answer the questions. There are no right answers and their answers will depend on what they actually observed.

## IV. Why?

Read this section of the *Laboratory Notebook* with your students.
Discuss any questions that might come up.

## V. Just For Fun

Students are to repeat the experiment, this time using stripes of different colored chalk dust.

Help the students crush different colors of chalk. Have them think about what arrangement of stripes they think will work best for this experiment (for example, horizontal, vertical, or diagonal stripes). Have them spread out the chalk dust in stripes of color in the arrangement they've chosen. They can repeat the experiment once, or they can repeat it two or more times, using different directions of stripes and other variations they may think of.

# Experiment 11

# Musical Glasses

**Materials Needed**

- 5 identical glass jars or drinking glasses
- water
- wooden drumstick, ruler, wooden spoon, or other wooden stick
- flat, unobstructed area for playing a game

**Optional**

- blindfold

## Objectives

In this unit, students will observe how sound travels differently through water and air.

The objectives of this lesson are for students to explore how:

- Sound travels through different media at different speeds with different frequencies.
- Sound energy can be transmitted through different media.

## Experiment

### I. Think About It

Read this section of the *Laboratory Notebook* with your students.

Explore open inquiry with questions such as the following:

- *What do you think will happen if you tap a glass with a wooden stick?*

- *Do you think the sound will be different if the glass has water in it or is empty? Why or why not?*

- *If you have several glasses with different amounts of water in them, do you think they will sound different from each other when tapped? Why or why not?*

- *Do you think sound will travel differently through glasses that have different amounts of water in them and are different sizes than glasses that are the same size? Why or why not?*

- *Do you think the sound will be different if you tap a glass with a metal spoon than if you tap it with a wooden stick?*

### II. Observe It

Read this section of the *Laboratory Notebook* with your students.

❶ Have the students line up five empty glasses or jars and then tap each one with a wooden stick. Have them try to use the same amount of force each time. If the glasses are all identical, they should observe similar sounds. Have them record their observations in the space provided.

❷ Have students pour water into 4 of the 5 glasses: full, 2/3 full, 1/2 full, and 1/3 full. The fifth glass will remain empty. The glasses should stay in this order for this part of the experiment.

PHYSICS

❸ In this step students will use the wooden stick to tap each glass in order, beginning with the full glass. Have them record their observations.

❹ Have the students tap the glasses several times, paying attention to the sound from each glass.

❺ In this step students will work with another person (the assistant). Have the students close their eyes or put on a blindfold. The assistant will rearrange the glasses, tap one, and have the students guess which glass was tapped. They will repeat this several times, tapping different glasses. After each tapping, the assistant will record which glass was tapped and which one the students guessed.

## Optional

Students can go around the room, tapping lightly on different items. Have them think about why the sound varies from object to object. Ask questions such as:

- *What is the object made of?*

- *Is it made of the same material on the outside and the inside?*

- *Is it solid or hollow?*

- *Is it soft or rigid?*

- *Is the sound high-pitched or low-pitched? Why?*

- *How would you describe the sound?*

## III. What Did You Discover?

Read this section of the *Laboratory Notebook* with your students.

Have the students answer the questions. There are no right answers and their answers will depend on what they actually observed.

## IV. Why?

Read this section of the *Laboratory Notebook* with your students.
Discuss any questions that might come up.

PHYSICS

## V. Just For Fun

In this experiment students will play the game *Marco Polo* to observe how sound travels through air and how it can be used for locating objects.

Find a large, flat, unobstructed area for students and friends to play this game. The student performing the experiment ("it") will keep their eyes closed or be blindfolded and yell "Marco!" The other players, who have fanned out, will respond by yelling "Polo!" Marco can be yelled repeatedly with the other players answering Polo until the student who is "it" finds and touches one of the other players.

Have the students think about how easy or difficult it was to use sound to locate a player and whether they think sound can be used as a device for locating objects. Have them record their observations and ideas in the space provided. There are no right answers

*PHYSICS*

## Experiment 12

# Separating Light

**Materials Needed**

- two prisms (glass or plastic)
- flashlight
- sunlight
- white wall, whiteboard, or other white surface
- colored pencils

## Objectives

In this experiment students will observe how white light can be separated into different wavelengths.

The objectives of this lesson are for students to:

- Use a simple tool to perform an experiment.
- Observe how white light can be split into different wavelengths that have different colors.

## Experiment

### I. Think About It

Read this section of the *Laboratory Notebook* with your students.

Ask questions such as the following to guide open inquiry:

- *What are the different colors in a rainbow?*

- *Do you think the colors in a rainbow can occur in a different order? Why or why not?*

- *When does a rainbow occur? Why?*

- *Do rainbows always occur when it rains? Why?*

- *What do you think makes a rainbow happen?*

- *Do you think you can make a rainbow happen? Why or why not?*

### II. Observe It

Read this section of the *Laboratory Notebook* with your students.

❶ Have the students shine the beam of a flashlight through the 90° bend of a prism. A white wall or board behind the prism is needed for the colors to show clearly. Getting everything positioned correctly can be a bit tricky. Help the students angle the prism so that the light will pass through it. The resulting rainbow will be cast behind the prism.

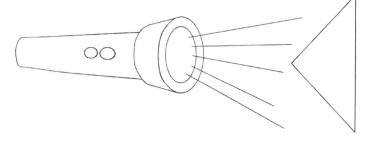

Have the students record what they see.

❷ Have the students direct sunlight through the 90° bend of the prism. Again have a white surface behind the prism. Have them record what they see.

❸ In the chart provided, have the students fill in which color wavelength is shorter or longer than another.

## III. What Did You Discover?

Read this section of the *Laboratory Notebook* with your students.
Have the students answer the questions based on what they actually observed.

## IV. Why?

Read this section of the *Laboratory Notebook* with your students.
Discuss any questions that might come up.

## V. Just For Fun

Students will shine the beam from a flashlight through two prisms arranged like those in the following illustration.

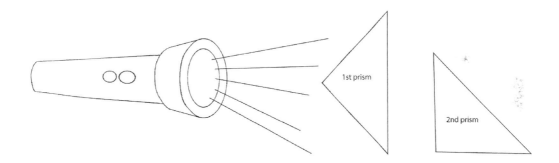

This time they will observe a double rainbow. The first rainbow will have red on the bottom and violet on top (or vice versa depending on how you shine the light through), and the second rainbow will be inverted—that is, exactly the opposite of the first rainbow. The prisms need to be lined up correctly for the double rainbow to appear, so you may need to help the students carefully adjust the angles and positions of the two prisms until the double rainbow is visible.

The inverted rainbow occurs because the second prism bends the colors a second time and flips them around. However, because the colors are already separated, they don't separate further. With two prisms you don't see a different rainbow than the one you saw from a single prism, but you see an inverted rainbow.

Have the students record their results.

# Bending Light

**Materials Needed**

- 3 small jars
- 180 ml (3/4 cup) vegetable oil
- 120 ml (1/2 cup) water
- 120 ml (1/2 cup) acetone (nail polish remover)
- food coloring
- drinking glass (a square glass is preferred, but a round glass will work)
- thin wooden stick (e.g., a kebab skewer)
- marking pen (or paper and tape) to label jars

## Objectives

In this experiment, students will observe how different liquids bend light.

The objectives of this lesson are for students to:

- Observe how light refracts in different liquids.
- Explore a scientific explanation for an observation (light bends and makes objects appear to bend).

## Experiment

### I. Think About It

Read this section of the *Laboratory Notebook* with your students.

Explore open inquiry with questions such as the following:

- *Do you think light can bend? Why or why not?*
- *Have you ever seen evidence that light bends? What did you observe?*
- *Do you think light always bends the same amount? Why or why not?*
- *Do you think the material that light is traveling through makes a difference in how much the light bends? Why or why not?*
- *Do you think it could be useful to know how much a given material will bend light? Why or why not?*

### II. Observe It

Read this section of the *Laboratory Notebook* with your students.

This experiment works best with a square glass. A round glass will work, but the curvature of the glass will cause additional distortion from refraction.

❶ Have the students label the three jars as "Water," "Oil," and "Acetone" and then put 60 ml (1/4 cup) of the appropriate liquid in each jar.

❷ Have the students add food coloring to the jar with the water in it.

❸ Have the students take the glass, tilt it, and carefully pour the acetone down the side of the glass. Have them set the glass down on a flat surface.

❹   Have the students put the wooden stick into the glass at an angle and record their observations in the box provided.

❺   Have the students pour the acetone back into its jar and wash and dry the glass.

❻-❼ Have the students repeat Steps ❸-❺ first with vegetable oil and then with water.

In the next part of the experiment students will observe how layers of different liquids refract light differently. The liquids need to be poured into the glass carefully so they form separate layers rather than mixing.

❽-❾ Have the students slowly pour the acetone down the side of the tilted glass followed by the vegetable oil. Have them carefully place the glass upright and put the wooden stick in the glass so the stick is tilted as much as possible. Have them record their observations.

❿   Have the students clean the glass and then repeat Steps ❽-❾ first pouring in the vegetable oil and then the water.

## III. What Did You Discover?

Read this section of the *Laboratory Notebook* with your students.
Have the students answer the questions based on what they actually observed.

## IV. Why?

Read this section of the *Laboratory Notebook* with your students.
Discuss any questions that might come up.

## V. Just For Fun

Have the students try to create three layers—acetone, vegetable oil, and water that they have added food coloring to. The students will need to add the different liquids very carefully in order for the acetone and water not to mix together.

Have the students keep the glass tilted while they slowly and carefully pour down the side of the glass first water, then vegetable oil, and finally acetone.

Have them record their observations.

# Predict the Weather

## Materials Needed

- large balloon (may substitute plastic wrap)
- glass jar
- scissors
- rubber band
- plastic straw
- toothpick
- tape
- index card

## Optional

- piece of cardboard

## Objectives

In this experiment, students will observe how to build a simple balloon barometer to record atmospheric pressure.

The objectives of this lesson are for students to:

- Observe how instruments help scientist make observations.
- Explore how changes in atmospheric pressure create weather.

## Experiment

### I. Think About It

Read this section of the *Laboratory Notebook* with your students.

Explore open inquiry with questions such as the following:

- *What happens on sunny days? Are there any clouds? If so, do these clouds turn into rain clouds? Why or why not?*

- *Do you feel different on sunny days than on cloudy days? Why or why not?*

- *Do you think the people who report the weather are usually right about what's going to happen? Why or why not?*

- *Do you think you have four different seasons where you live? Why or why not? How is the weather different in each of the seasons?*

- *What have you noticed when a storm starts and when it ends?*

- *What do you think would happen if the weather stayed the same every day of the year?*

### II. Observe It

Read this section of the *Laboratory Notebook* with your students.

Help your students build the balloon barometer. It is important that the balloon is stretched tightly over the rim of the jar and firmly secured. No air must escape from the glass jar during the experiment. If a balloon is not available, you can use plastic wrap instead.

❶ Have the students cut the top off a large balloon. The piece of the balloon needs to be large enough that when stretched over the mouth of the jar, it hangs down far enough on the sides of the jar that it can be fastened securely with a rubber band.

GEOLOGY

❷   Have the students stretch the balloon top over the mouth of the jar and fasten it securely with the rubber band so that no air can escape from the jar.

❸   Have the students measure and cut the straw to 10 cm (4 in.) in length, tape a toothpick securely to one end of the straw, and tape the other end of the straw to the balloon on the jar. The end of the straw with the toothpick will extend beyond the edge of the jar.

❹   Have the students draw a line across the middle of the index card and write "High pressure" above the line and "Low pressure" below the line.

❺   Students will use the toothpick and the index card to observe changes in atmospheric pressure. Have the students position the index card so the toothpick lines up with the line they drew on the index card and then fasten the index card to a wall or to a piece of cardboard propped up against a wall. The toothpick is the needle of the barometer.

The barometer should be set up in a location where it won't need to be moved during the course of the experiment and where it does not get any direct sunlight.

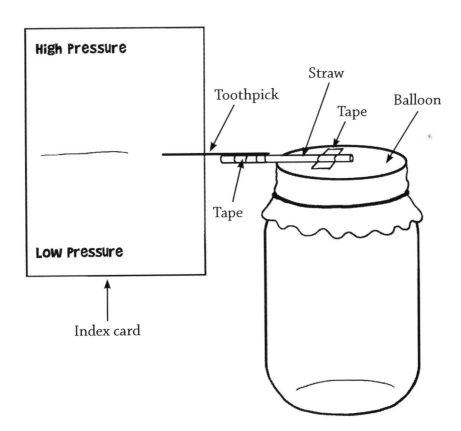

❻ Every day for a week, students will observe changes in the position of the barometer needle (toothpick) and record these along with the weather conditions. It may be helpful to have them put a mark on the index card each day indicating the position of the toothpick along with the date.

As the atmospheric pressure changes, the barometer needle (toothpick) will move up and down. The atmospheric pressure of the air sealed in the jar remains the same, but as the pressure outside the jar changes, the balloon will move up or down relative to the rim of the glass jar. The atmospheric pressure on the day the jar is sealed may have an effect on the results of the experiment. If weather conditions don't vary much, students may not see much movement of the barometer needle.

❼-❽ Have the students review their observations, noting how the position of the barometer correlated to the weather. For the next week have them predict coming weather changes by noting the position of the barometer and comparing this to their previous observations. Have them record the barometer readings and their predictions for each day. In the last box they will record how the weather actually changed and compare it to their predictions.

## III. What Did You Discover?

Read this section of the *Laboratory Notebook* with your students.

Have the students answer the questions. There are no right answers, and their answers will be based on what they actually observed.

## IV. Why?

Read this section of the *Laboratory Notebook* with your students.
Discuss any questions that might come up.

## V. Just For Fun

In this experiment students will observe cloud formations to see if they can find a relationship between the type of clouds and the weather that follows.

Each day for a week or two, have them draw the clouds they observe and note the weather conditions. At the end of the experiment, have them review their notes to look for cloud/weather relationships.

GEOLOGY

# Experiment 15

# Unintended Consequences

## Materials Needed

- scissors
- tape
- 2 small baskets, hats, or other containers to hold game pieces
- pair of dice

## Optional

- colored pencils

## Objectives

In this unit, students will observe a food chain and how a change to a part of an ecosystem can bring about unintended consequences.

The objectives of this lesson are for students to explore how:

- Different organisms are part of a food chain.
- A food chain can be disrupted by changes in the ecosystem.

## Experiment

### I. Think About It

Read this section of the *Laboratory Notebook* with your students.

Guide open inquiry with questions such as the following:

- *Do you think animals depend on each other? In what ways?*

- *Do you think that in Africa lions need to live near zebras? Why or why not?*

- *Do you think zebras would be better off if there were no lions? Why or why not?*

- *What do you think would happen to the plants and animals in Africa if there were a long drought? Why?*

- *What do you think would happen to the plants and animals in Africa if there were a lot more rain than usual? Why?*

- *Do you think bringing one new organism into the savanna could change the ecosystem? Why or why not?*

### II. Observe It

Read this section of the *Laboratory Notebook* with your students.

In this experiment students will play a board game called *Ruler of the Savanna* to learn about the interrelatedness of organisms in an ecosystem.

❶ Have the students cut out each token and place all the tokens in a basket, hat, or other container.

GEOLOGY

❷  Have the students cut out each unintended consequences card and place all the cards in a different basket, hat, or other container.

❸  Have them cut out the two parts of the game board and tape them together.

❹  Go over the Groups, Instructions, and Rules for the game and have the students play the game one or more times.

## III. What Did You Discover?

Read this section of the *Laboratory Notebook* with your students.
Discuss any questions that might come up.

## IV. Why?

Read this section of the *Laboratory Notebook* with your students.
Discuss any questions that might come up.

## V. Just For Fun

Students are to play the game again after first making their own unintended consequences cards from new situations that they come up with. The idea is for them to think about how making a change in the ecosystem can bring about unexpected results. The situation they think of may or may not be one that might actually occur. There are no right answers. Students can also make some new tokens with different African savanna organisms on them. Help the students think about which trophic level the new organisms would be in.

—or—

Students can create a new game based on the Rules and Instructions for *Ruler of the Savanna*. Have them choose an ecosystem they'd like to use as the basis for the game. This may be an ecosystem in your area or another ecosystem that interests them. Ask questions to help the students think about what organisms to represent, what trophic level the organisms are in, and some unintended consequences that might occur. Students may want to make changes to the rules or instructions. Again, there are no right answers.

GEOLOGY

# Wind or Sun?

## Materials Needed

- Two model kits selected from the list below. (Availability may change. Similar kits may be substituted.)

**Windmill Generator Kit**: HomeScience Tools
http://www.hometrainingtools.com/windmill-generator-kit/p/KT-GSWIND/

**Wind Turbine Science Kit**: HomeScience Tools
http://www.hometrainingtools.com/wind-turbine-science-kit/p/KT-WIN-TURB/

**KidWind Basic Wind Experiment Kit**: Vernier
http://www.vernier.com/products/kidwind/wind-energy/kits/kw-bwx/

**KidWind MINI Wind Turbine**: Vernier
http://www.vernier.com/products/kidwind/wind-energy/kits/kw-mwt/

**SunnySide Up Solar Car**: SunWind
http://sunwindsolar.com/sunny-side-up/

**Chariots of the Sun**: SunWind
http://sunwindsolar.com/chariots-of-the-sun/

**Solar Powered Car**: HomeScience Tools
http://www.hometrainingtools.com/solar-powered-car/p/EL-SOLRCAR/

## Objectives

In this experiment students will build a model wind turbine or solar powered car to explore renewable energy sources.

The objectives of this lesson are for students to:

- Observe how science and engineering combine to create technologies.
- Explore how renewable energy sources work.

## Experiment

### I. Think About It

Read this section of the *Laboratory Notebook* with your students.

Explore open inquiry with questions such as the following:

- *What type of climate do we live in?*
- *How many windy days do we have?*
- *How strong is the wind?*
- *Are there areas nearby where it is more windy?*
- *How many sunny days do we have?*
- *How bright is the sunshine?*
- *Are there places that get more sunshine?*

### II. Observe It

Read this section of the *Laboratory Notebook* with your students.

❶ Help your students select and build one of the suggested kits. It is possible to put together your own kit; however, purchasing a kit with machined parts that all fit together well and function properly is recommended. Other kits may be substituted.

❷ Have the students test their model to see how it works and what the different parts do.

❸ Have the students record their observations in the box provided.

GEOLOGY

## III. What Did You Discover?

Read this section of the *Laboratory Notebook* with your students.

Have the students answer the questions. There are no right answers and their answers will depend on what they actually observed.

## IV. Why?

Read this section of the *Laboratory Notebook* with your students.
Discuss any questions that might come up.

## V. Just For Fun

Have the students choose another model to build. They can choose one of the same type or a different one. Help them follow the instructions to assemble the model.

Once the model is complete, have the students test it and observe how it works.

Have them review their observations of the first model and compare the two models. If one is wind powered and one solar, have them think about how they are different and how they are the same. If both are of the same type, have them compare the parts in each and whether one works better than the other and why. How are they different and how are they the same?

Students can try making modifications to their models to see how changes affect the way the models function. Can they think of a modification that might make either model work better? Have them try it. It may work or the model may not function afterwards. Finding out what doesn't work is important for scientific discovery. Discuss the results with the students.

GEOLOGY

# Experiment 17

## Take Out the Trash!

**Materials Needed**

**Optional**

- small notebook

## Objectives

In this experiment, students will observe how daily use of materials and foods generates trash.

The objectives of this lesson are for students to:

- Observe how individuals impact Earth.
- Observe how pollution is cumulative and builds over time.

## Experiment

### I. Think About It

Read this section of the *Laboratory Notebook* with your students.

Explore open inquiry with questions such as the following:

- *What do you think "trash" is?"*
- *What kinds of trash have you seen?*
- *What kinds of trash do you make?*
- *How much trash do you think you create in one day, one week, one month, or a year?*
- *What do we do with trash in our home, community, city, state, country?*
- *Do you think trash creates problems? Why or why not?*

### II. Observe It

Read this section of the *Laboratory Notebook* with your students.

This experiment will take place over the course of three weeks. A small notebook can be used to record items when students are away from home. Their observations can be recorded later in the *Laboratory Notebook*.

❶ Have the students record all the trash they generate in one week—how much and what types.

❷ Have the students record all the trash they generate this week. This time they will list which items can be recycled and which cannot.

❸ At the end of Week 2, have the students compare their observations from Week 1 and Week 2 and note similarities and differences. Help them observe how much of the trash is recyclable compared to the amount of trash that is not.

*GEOLOGY*

❹ This week, as students record the recyclable and non-recyclable trash they produce, they will record any ideas they have about how they could reduce the amount of trash produced.

Help students understand that living without generating trash would be practically impossible in modern society. However, remind students that it is important to reduce the amount of trash produced and that it can be interesting to explore ways to reduce the production of trash, dispose of trash, and turn it back into usable materials.

## III. What Did You Discover?

Read this section of the *Laboratory Notebook* with your students.

Have the students answer the questions. There are no right answers and their answers will depend on what they actually observed.

## IV. Why?

Read this section of the *Laboratory Notebook* with your students.
Discuss any questions that might come up.

## V. Just For Fun

Have the students use their imagination to think of ways to dispose of all the trash in the world. Encourage them to explore their ideas freely even if you know they won't work. Using the imagination is an important part of doing science.

GEOLOGY

# Experiment 18

# Up, Up, and Away!

**Materials Needed**

**One or more of the following rocket kits**

- **High-Fly Rocket Kit: HomeScience Tools**
  http://www.hometrainingtools.com/high-fly-rocket-kit/p/KT-FHROCK/

- **001225 - Alpha Rocket: Estes Rockets** (engine sold separately)
  http://www.estesrockets.com/rockets/001225-alphar

- **000651 - Der Red Max Rocket: Estes Rockets** (engine sold separately)
  http://www.estesrockets.com/rockets/kits/skill-1/der-red-maxtm

- **000810- 220 Swift Rocket: Estes Rockets** (additional parts sold separately)
  http://www.estesrockets.com/000810-220-swifttm

- Tools for assembly depending on kit selected

Note: Other kits may be substituted

## Objectives

In this experiment students will build a model rocket and explore the challenges scientists and engineers encounter while launching objects into the sky.

The objectives of this lesson are to have students:

- Observe how science and engineering combine.
- Explore how models are used in science and engineering.

## Experiment

### I. Think About It

Read this section of the *Laboratory Notebook* with your students.

Explore open inquiry with questions such as the following:

- *How far do you think a rocket can travel?*
- *Why do you think some rockets can travel farther than others?*
- *Why do you think some rockets can travel faster than others?*
- *If you were designing a new rocket, what parts of the rocket would you have to think about? Why?*
- *How big do you think a rocket needs to be to launch a small pebble?*
- *How big do you think a rocket needs to be to launch a stuffed animal?*
- *How big do you think a rocket needs to be to launch a watermelon?*

### II. Observe It

Read this section of the *Laboratory Notebook* with your students.

Help the students choose one or more model rocket kits from the list provided. A different kit not on the list may be substituted.

Help the students follow the instructions that come with the kit to assemble and launch their model rocket. It is possible to put together your own kit; however, purchasing a kit is recommended because the parts will fit together well and the model will work properly.

ASTRONOMY

## III. What Did You Discover?

Read this section of the *Laboratory Notebook* with the students.

Have the students answer the questions. There are no "right" answers and their answers will depend on what they actually observed.

## IV. Why?

Read this section of the *Laboratory Notebook* with your students.
Discuss any questions that may come up.

## V. Just For Fun

Ask questions to help students think about what changes they might make to their model rocket to redesign it. Have them list their ideas in the space provided.

Have the students review their list of ideas, choose one idea, use it to modify the model rocket, and then test the rocket. Have them follow this procedure for each modification they want to test. Have them record their results for each test.

Encourage students to use their imagination even if you know the idea won't work. Experimenting is an important part of science, and scientists learn as much or more from experiments that don't have the expected results as they do from experiments that work as expected.

## Experiment 19

# How Far?

**Materials Needed**

- tape
- scissors
- marking pen

**Optional**

- 2-3 push pins or tacks

## Objectives

In this experiment, students will observe how parallax can be used to measure distance.

The objectives of this lesson are for students to:

- Estimate distance using simple tools.
- Explore graphing and plotting data to observe a trend.

## Experiment

### I. Think About It

Read this section of the *Laboratory Notebook* with your students.

Explore open inquiry with questions such as the following:

- *Do you think only astronomers use parallax to measure distances? Why or why not?*

- *Do you think parallax could be used to measure something close to you? Why or why not?*

- *Do you think there is a way you could use parallax in your everyday life? Why or why not?*

- *What are some examples of times when you might want to estimate how far away something is?*

### II. Observe It

Read this section of the *Laboratory Notebook* with your students.

In this experiment students will learn a quick way to estimate distances using parallax.

❶-❷ Have the students practice observing the parallax effect. Have them choose an object some distance away and hold their arm fully extended in front of them with their thumb up so it is in front of the object. Have them close one eye and then switch eyes. Have them record their observations. They should notice that their thumb appears to move with respect to the distant object. Have them repeat with several different objects at varying distances.

❸-❹ Have the students cut out the ruler at the end of this section of the *Laboratory Notebook,* tape it together, and fill in the number 4 on both sides of the ruler. Help them find a wall with enough space that they can walk 20 heel to toe steps from it. Have them tape or tack the ruler to this wall at eye level.

ASTRONOMY ☆☆○☆☆

❺   Have the students use their feet as measuring devices with their heel to toe equal to one "foot." Have them stand with their back to the wall the ruler is taped to, walk heel to toe 5 "feet" away from the wall, and turn around.

❻-❼   Next they will extend one arm to its full length and hold their thumb up. They will close one eye and look at their thumb with the other eye, lining their thumb up with the "0" on the ruler. Then they will switch eyes and note the number on the ruler that their thumb is now aligned with. Have them record this number in the table provided.

❽-❾   Have the students repeat Steps ❻-❼ first taking 5 more steps (for a total of 10 "feet") and then taking 10 more steps (for a total of 20 "feet"). Have them record their results each time.

❿   Help the students plot their data on the graph provided.

## III. What Did You Discover?

Read this section of the *Laboratory Notebook* with your students.
Discuss any questions that might come up.

Question ❺: Have them draw a line through the three data points on the graph. This line should be more or less straight.

## IV. Why?

Read this section of the *Laboratory Notebook* with your students.
Discuss any questions that might come up.

## V. Just For Fun

Have the students use the parallax method described in the *Why* section to try to determine how far a distant object is from where they are standing.

# Experiment 20

# Finding Exoplanets

## Materials Needed

- computer with internet access

(Note: This experiment uses
a project on the Zooniverse
website. Projects and websites
change from time to time.
If this project becomes
unavailable, you can look on
Zooniverse for a different
astronomy project or do a
browser search for citizen
science astronomy projects for
children.)

## Objectives

In this experiment, students will explore how astronomers search for exoplanets. Students will participate as citizen scientists in an online project on the Zooniverse website.

The objectives of this lesson are to have students:

- Explore an online data source.
- Learn how to identify an exoplanet using an online database.

## Experiment

### I. Think About It

Read this section of the *Laboratory Notebook* with your students.

Explore open inquiry with questions such as the following:

> - *What kinds of tools do you think astronomers use to find planets that are outside our solar system?*
>
> - *Do you think exoplanets could have been detected 100 years ago? Why or why not?*
>
> - *What do you think would be needed for a planet to support life as we know it?*
>
> - *Do you think a planet could support some form of life that is different from life that exists on Earth? If so, what would it be like?*

### II. Observe It

Read this section of the *Laboratory Notebook* with your students.

**Exoplanet Explorers** is an astronomy project on the Zooniverse website. This project asks citizen scientists to use data collected from the Kepler spacecraft K2 mission to help astronomers find exoplanets.

❶ Help the students find the Zooniverse website at www.zooniverse.org.

❷ Have them click on the **Register** tab on the top menu bar and help them fill in the required information to become a Zooniverse citizen scientist. In the box on the following page in the *Laboratory Notebook,* have the students record their login name and password so they can return to Zooniverse at any time. Their login information can also be used to access other Zooniverse projects.

ASTRONOMY

❸   Have them click on the **Projects** tab on the top menu bar, then click the right arrow to find the **Space** icon. Have them click on this icon and then on the **Exoplanet Explorers K2** project.

❹   Read the **About** pages and the FAQs with the students. Help them explore the **Talk** and **Collect** areas.

❺   Once the students have explored the different project areas, have them click on the **Classify** tab. A box titled **Welcome to Exoplanet Explorers** will appear. This is the project tutorial. If this box doesn't appear, have them click the **Show Project Tutorial** box at the bottom of the screen.

❻   Read all the pages of the tutorial with the students.

❼   Have the students click on the **Field Guide** tab on the right. Clicking on each example type will bring up the information for it. (The back arrow at the top can be used to return to the example choices.) Studying all the examples will help the students become familiar with the characteristics being looked for.

❽   Have the students begin classifying transiting planets. They will look at the images on the left side of the screen and select **yes** or **no**, then click **Done**. If they want to change their answer, have them click **More**, otherwise click **Next**.

It takes practice and patience to figure out how to select data representative of an exoplanet. Encourage your students to keep trying, but allow breaks if needed. Students can return to the project at any time.

❾   In the box provided, have students make notes and sketches of their observations.

## III. What Did You Discover?

Read this section of the *Laboratory Notebook* with your students.

Have the students answer the questions. There are no right answers and their answers will depend on what they actually observed.

## IV. Why?

Read this section of the *Laboratory Notebook* with your students.
Discuss any questions that may come up.

## V. Just For Fun

Students are to imagine they are an astronomer looking for signs of intelligent life on exoplanets. Encourage them to use their imagination freely in thinking about how they would do this. New discoveries in science start with new ideas. There are no right answers. Let the students explore their ideas even if you think they won't work.

## Experiment 21

# Build a Robot!

### Materials Needed

One of the following robot kits or a different kit of your choice

http://www.hometrainingtools.com/robo-link-robot-kit/p/KT-ROBLINK/

http://www.hometrainingtools.com/jungle-robot-kit/p/EL-JUNGLE/

http://www.robotshop.com/en/2wd-beginner-robot-chassis.html

http://www.robotshop.com/en/em4-educational-motorized-robot-kit.html

## Objectives

In this experiment, students will build their own robot and explore the challenges of designing robots for use in space projects.

The objectives of this lesson are for students to:

- Observe how science contributes to technology.
- Explore how science, engineering, and technology are used in space exploration.

## Experiment

### I. Think About It

Read this section of the *Laboratory Notebook* with your students.

Explore open inquiry with the following:

- *What have you seen robots doing in the movies or on TV?*

- *Do you think there are robots that can really do these things? Why or why not?*

- *Do you think robots could be useful for space exploration? Why or why not?*

- *Do you think robots in space could do things that humans can't? Why or why not? What things could robots do?*

- *Do you think scientists will be able to make robots that can think? Why or why not?*

### II. Observe It

Read this section of the *Laboratory Notebook* with your students.

❶ Help the students select a robot from the list provided or find a different one.

❷ Have the students assemble the robot and play with it to see what functions it can perform. Have them notice what their robot can and cannot do. Does it roll, walk, or jump? Can it climb, move objects, turn around when it encounters an obstacle? Have them record their observations.

❸ Have the students record what the robot cannot do.

ASTRONOMY

❹-❺ Have the students observe what the robot has for a power source and what materials the robot is made of. Have them record their observations.

❻ Have the students think about what modifications they would make to the robot if they were able to and what else they would like the robot to do. Have them record their ideas.

## III. What Did You Discover?

Read this section of the *Laboratory Notebook* with your students.

Have the students answer the questions. There are no right answers and their answers will depend on what they actually observed.

## IV. Why?

Read this section of the *Laboratory Notebook* with your students.
Discuss any questions that might come up.

## V. Just For Fun

Have the students modify their robot so it can carry, push, or pull an object.

Have them think about whether the robot can be modified to perform any additional functions and then try the modifications they think of.

Have them record their observations.

## Experiment 22

## Winning
## the Nobel Prize

**Materials Needed**

- Laboratory Notebook

## Objectives

In this experiment students will take a critical look at the experiments they performed and will explore their own discoveries.

The objectives of this lesson are for students to:

- Evaluate their own data.
- Explore the nature of scientific discovery.

## Experiment

### I. Think About It

Read this section of the *Laboratory Notebook* with your students.

Explore open inquiry with questions such as the following:

- *What is your favorite experiment from this book? Why?*

- *Do you think you made scientific discoveries by doing the experiments in this book? Why or why not?*

- *Do you think doing these experiments helped you better understand scientific concepts? Why or why not?*

- *Do you think the experiments that did not work were important? Why or why not?*

- *How do you think the Nobel Prize encourages scientists to keep working towards discoveries that are the "greatest benefit to mankind?"*

### II. Observe It

Read this section of the *Laboratory Notebook* with your students.

Help your students evaluate their own work. In answering the questions students don't have to list every experiment that fits but should at least select several. You can guide them to think about their favorite experiments, ones they had difficulty with, and ones they didn't like that much. Did they learn different things from performing these different types of experiments?

❶-❷ Have the students look through their *Laboratory Notebook* and observe those experiments that "worked" and those that didn't "work." Have them record their observations.

❸ Have the students think about what they discovered from both the experiments that worked and those that didn't.

❹ Have the students pick one experiment that did not work. Help them think about why it did not work and whether they could make changes that would improve the experiment and make it work better.

❺ Have the students look through their *Laboratory Notebook* for those experiments that they think involved two or more scientific disciplines. Have them record their observations.

## III. What Did You Discover?

Read this section of the *Laboratory Notebook* with your students.

Have students answer the questions based on what they actually observed rather than what they thought should have happened. There are no right answers.

## IV. Why?

Read this section of the *Laboratory Notebook* with your students.
Discuss any questions that might come up.

## V. Just For Fun

Have the students imagine that they are being considered for a Nobel Prize. Have them write, draw, or create a video explaining their favorite experiment as if they were presenting their work to the Nobel Committee.

# More REAL SCIENCE-4-KIDS Books
## by Rebecca W. Keller, PhD

**Building Blocks Series** yearlong study program — each Student Textbook has accompanying Laboratory Notebook, Teacher's Manual, Lesson Plan, Study Notebook, Quizzes, and Graphics Package

Exploring Science Book K (Activity Book)
Exploring Science Book 1
Exploring Science Book 2
Exploring Science Book 3
Exploring Science Book 4
Exploring Science Book 5
Exploring Science Book 6
Exploring Science Book 7
Exploring Science Book 8

**Focus On Series** unit study program — each title has a Student Textbook with accompanying Laboratory Notebook, Teacher's Manual, Lesson Plan, Study Notebook, Quizzes, and Graphics Package

Focus On Elementary Chemistry
Focus On Elementary Biology
Focus On Elementary Physics
Focus On Elementary Geology
Focus On Elementary Astronomy

Focus On Middle School Chemistry
Focus On Middle School Biology
Focus On Middle School Physics
Focus On Middle School Geology
Focus On Middle School Astronomy

Focus On High School Chemistry

## Super Simple Science Experiments

21 Super Simple Chemistry Experiments
21 Super Simple Biology Experiments
21 Super Simple Physics Experiments
21 Super Simple Geology Experiments
21 Super Simple Astronomy Experiments
101 Super Simple Science Experiments

**Note:** A few titles may still be in production.

## Gravitas Publications Inc.
www.gravitaspublications.com
www.realscience4kids.com